P9-AOW-611

Thanks for remembering
the sacrifice of others.
Cindy Sheehan

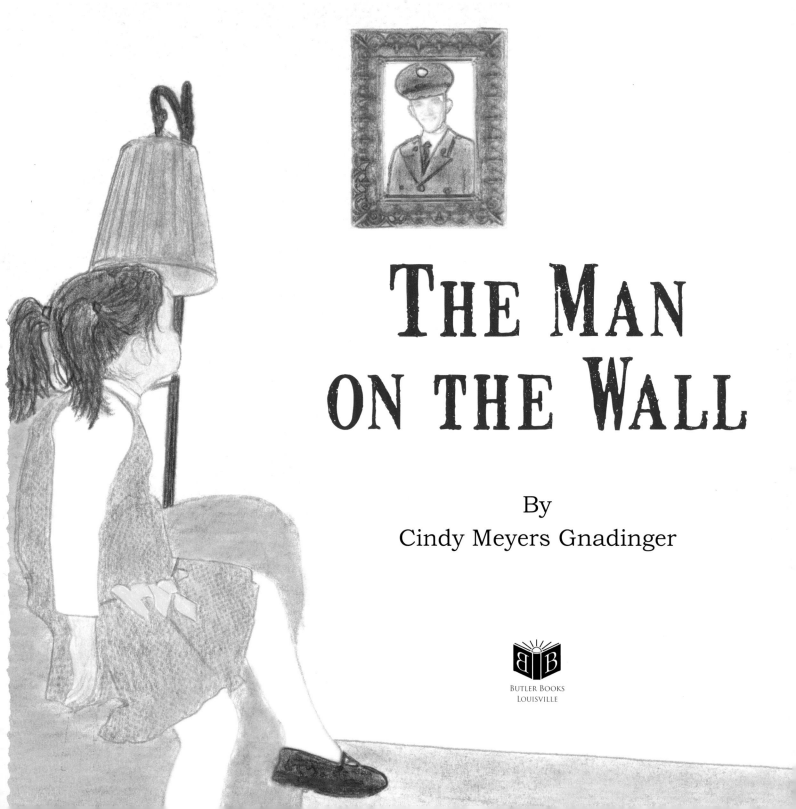

THE MAN
ON THE WALL

By
Cindy Meyers Gnadinger

BUTLER BOOKS
LOUISVILLE

ACKNOWLEDGMENTS

I owe special thanks to my mother, for answering my many questions; to Ouida and my other aunts, for sharing their memories with me; and to my family, for graciously serving as models for this book's illustrations. My appreciation to Caroline for her superb acting skills and to Madison, the perfect mini me.

- CMG

ISBN 978-1-935497-17-2
Printed in Canada

Manufactured by Friesens Corporation
Manufactured in Altona, MB, Canada in April 2010
Job # 55315

Book design by Scott Stortz

Published by:
Butler Books
P.O. Box 7311
Louisville, KY 40207
(502) 897–9393
Fax (502) 897–9797

www.butlerbooks.com

For Ronnie,
and all the others who went to war
and never came home

"It's time to go!" That call from my dad signaled our Sunday ritual when I was a child. We would pile into the family station wagon and off we'd go. I loved going to my grandparents' house. There was always a crowd at their home. When your mother is the oldest of twelve children, you end up with a lot of relatives!

On Sundays, their house would fill up with people–people talking, people laughing, and people playing. At family gatherings, we filled all the rooms in the house and even spilled out into the yard. Our cars lined both sides of the street. When our family got together, everyone in the neighborhood knew it!

On one of those Sunday visits to Mom and Pop's, I noticed my uncle talking with my grandmother. As she peered out the kitchen window, he gently put his arm around her and whispered, "Mother, he's not coming home." She dropped her head and walked away without saying a word. The room fell quiet.

"Who's not coming home?" I wondered. *"Who are they talking about?"* Then, suddenly, I realized. *"The man on the wall. They're talking about the man on the wall!"*

I never paid much attention to the picture of the man on the wall at my grandparents' house. He was there for as long as I could remember, smiling down at me.

Later that afternoon, I took my mother into the den. I pointed to the picture and asked her, "Who's that man on the wall?" She stared silently for a moment at the picture of the handsome man in his uniform and hat. I waited for her answer. Then she crouched down next to me and said, "That man was your uncle. He went to war and never came home. His name was Ronnie."

No one talked much about Ronnie at my grandparents' house. "It makes your grandmother too sad," I was told. I already knew that. I saw the sadness in her eyes when she walked away from the window that day. I made sure never to ask her questions about the man on the wall. However, through the years, I learned a lot about him. He had an adventurous spirit and was full of life!

Ronnie was one of my mother's brothers. He was the third child in a family of twelve children. He was a typical, all-American boy growing up in the 1950s. It seemed he made friends with everyone he met. With his outgoing personality and contagious smile, he never met a stranger.

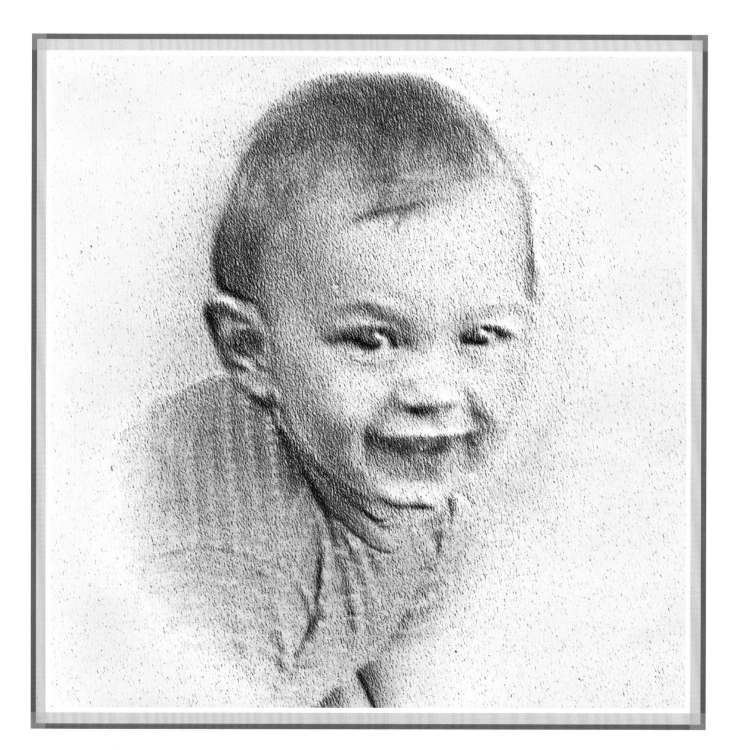

Ronnie was an active child who was extremely curious, evidenced by the fact that he would take things apart and put them back together. He wanted to know how everything worked.

With all of his brothers and sisters, Ronnie always had a playmate. He occupied himself by climbing trees, riding bikes, and playing in his neighborhood.

Ronnie had a fascination with animals. When my grandmother would do laundry, she would often find frogs and worms in his pockets.

Once she found a jar of praying mantis' eggs he had stored in the basement. No one knew that one praying mantis egg could produce 200 babies! When the eggs hatched, there were hundreds of tiny mantids flying and hopping all over the house. An exterminator had to be called in to clear them out. Needless to say, Pop was not happy!

Ronnie found a baby squirrel and made it his pet. He fed it, played with it, and watched it grow.

"Don't you forget, that squirrel is a wild animal and it will scratch you if you're not careful," his mother warned him. But Ronnie wasn't worried. That squirrel would climb down his back, up his shirt, and even sit on top of his head!

He and his squirrel were quite a team. Together, they entertained everyone in the neighborhood.

Playing music was one of his hobbies. When he was young, he would sit outside on the picnic table and play his guitar for hours. He never had formal lessons, but taught himself how to play.

As a teenager, he and his friends formed a band. They played music at church picnics, store openings and parties around town.

Ronnie and his siblings attended elementary school near their home, so they would walk to school each day. When he finished eighth grade, he went on to high school. After high school, he was ready for a new adventure, so he moved away from home and enrolled in college.

While taking college classes, Ronnie found a job working at a funeral home. He would drive the ambulance, assist in medical emergencies, and transport deceased people to the cemetery.

"You do what?" people would ask. Some people thought working for a funeral home was a creepy job. They asked him if it frightened him to be alone in a car with a dead person. "Those people never bother me," he would respond with a grin.

The funeral home where Ronnie worked was next door to a beauty shop, and one afternoon he was introduced to a young lady who worked there. After meeting her, he was eager to make an appointment for his next haircut. Not long after that meeting, Ronnie began dating the hairdresser and he soon realized that he loved her. At a drive-in restaurant one evening, he asked her to marry him, and she said, "Yes." They were married soon thereafter. Life sure was good!

During the 1960s, the United States was at war in Vietnam. There was a great deal of controversy surrounding the war. Some Americans were opposed to it and felt our country should not be involved. Many men in the United States were sent to fight in Vietnam.

Three months after he was married, Ronnie received a letter from the United States government. He knew immediately that it was a draft notification. Being drafted meant that he would have to leave his wife and family to help America fight in the war.

In the months that followed, Ronnie had to quit his job, pack up his belongings and prepare for his two-year absence. Just before he left for Vietnam, he and his wife visited his parents and family members. They attended Ash Wednesday church service as a family, where everyone quietly prayed for his safety.

Afterward, they gathered at his parents' home to spend time together and to say goodbye. "Can you hang on to my guitar until I get back?" Ronnie asked his mother. He handed it to her for safekeeping. She promised him it would be there when he returned.

Later that night, everyone went to bed. Pop couldn't sleep. He paced the floor all night long. He wanted desperately to do something but he didn't know what to do. *"Maybe I should tell him not to go,"* he wondered. *"Maybe I should tell him to run to Canada and stay until the war is over, like some of the others are doing."*

He didn't want his son to experience the horrors of war or risk losing his life.   Pop knew how terrible it was going to be because he, too, had been drafted and fought in World War II. In the end, he knew Ronnie had to go.

The next morning, as Ronnie walked out the door to leave for Vietnam, he turned back to the family members who were gathered together. Ronnie smiled at them and said, "I'll see you all later. Don't worry about me, I'll be back soon."   As he stepped out the door he heard them all respond, "Hurry back." Bye, Ronnie." "Be careful." "We love you." "Write soon."

He waved goodbye and closed the door. Suddenly, the house felt quiet and empty.

Ronnie arrived in a city called Saigon, where the fighting was harsh. Stories about Vietnam were on television every day and the news reported that many people were dying there. His family anxiously waited to hear from him to find out that he was safe.

Once he was settled in Vietnam with his unit, he wrote letters telling about his experiences. His wife waited eagerly each day to read the letters he sent.

His family wrote to him, baked cookies to send him, and prayed for him. They had the local newspaper sent overseas. They hoped it might cheer him up if he could read about events taking place back home.

Several weeks after Ronnie left, his mother and sister got together to bake cookies to send him. Without warning, two military officers arrived at the door. When his mother saw them, she froze, her heart raced, and she felt sick. She knew what their visit could mean.

The officers had a message for Ronnie's wife. "She doesn't live here. She is living with her parents until he returns home from the war," his sister explained. "Please tell us the news you have about him," they begged.

The officers would not share the information with his parents. They explained that they could only speak with his wife because she was his next of kin. The officers left to find her. Ronnie's parents and family members waited desperately by the phone for the news.

Everyone was worried. They knew that officers never come with good news. For nearly three hours, they sat by the telephone and waited for the call from Ronnie's wife.

Some of his younger siblings were confused. "What does this mean?" they asked. Pop explained that it was possible that Ronnie had been injured and the officers were coming to let them know this. Pop mentioned that it was also a possibility that he might be missing in action. He added, "Missing in action means the military officials can't find the soldier. When soldiers are missing, they could either be hurt somewhere and unable to report to their sergeant or, even worse, they may have been taken by the enemy as a prisoner."

No one mentioned the very worst scenario. Everyone knew that Ronnie might have been killed. They prayed that he was still alive. They prayed that he had not been captured and taken as a prisoner of war. They prayed that he was only slightly injured. That was the best they could hope for.

Finally, the phone rang. Pop nervously answered it and received the news from Ronnie's wife. The officers told her that Ronnie was missing in action, and when they were able to locate him, they promised to notify her. The family was devastated to hear this, but at least there was hope. He could still be alive!

For weeks, his family and friends prayed for him and waited for further word. Every time the phone rang, they jumped and wondered, *"Could this be news about Ronnie?"* They worried through each long day, waiting and speculating.

It was nearly three weeks before the officers returned. This time, the news was not good. Their hope was gone. He was never coming home.

The officers explained that Ronnie, who was serving as a radio telephone operator, was with his platoon heading to a location where heavy fighting was taking place. A helicopter brought them in and hovered near the ground so the soldiers could jump out. The helicopter left and the soldiers headed off on foot toward the fighting. The officers believed that someone in his platoon, they didn't know who, stepped on a land mine and it exploded. Ronnie was killed instantly. He was only 22 years old.

The local newspapers reported the terrible news. Many people in the community mourned his death. "How can this be true?" people asked. It was hard to believe that someone so energetic and full of life was simply gone, in an instant.

CUMBERLAND COUNTY

CUMBERLAND MOUNTAINS

CUMBERLAND LAKE
DALE HOLLOW LAKE

FIRST OIL WELL
Strawberries

Broilers

UME NO. 47   BURKESVILLE, KENTUCKY 42717 THURSDAY, MARCH 23, 1967

KILLED IN VIET NAM

Hiram Parrish Appointed

Hiram Parrish, prominent Cumberland County farmer, has been appointed as Cumberland Co. Judge by Gov. Edward N. Breathitt. He was sworn in at the Governor's office in Frankfort Monday noon this week.

Mr. Parrish, a Democrat, was appointed to fill the office as interim judge until the county voters can cast ballots at a General Election in November, to fill the vacancy created by the death of the late Judge W. C. Stearns. He was a Republican, and took office Jan. 1, 1966.

Mr. Parrish was recommended by the Democratic organization in the council to Gov. Breathitt, since, in the case of death, the Governor is required by law to appoint an interim sucessor. Mr. Parrish is well known to be much interested in improvements in the county and takes an active part in many civic activities.

A Primary Election for the

3000 GALLONS OF MILK DOWN THE
of the 150 farmers of this area, NFO
ning and destroyed about 3000 gallons

The first "holding action" of the Cumberland Co. National Farmers Organization (NFO) was staged in Burkesville Tuesday morning of this

A train brought Ronnie's body back on Easter Sunday. Although it was midnight when the train arrived, countless people were waiting at the station. Cars were lined up as far as the eye could see. The people came to honor him and thank him for his service to America.

As his body was transported to the funeral home, a long procession of cars followed behind through the quiet, dark night.

Ronnie was buried a few days later in his hometown, with full military honors and a 21-gun salute. His wife accepted the Purple Heart medal on his behalf.

The following weeks were filled with indescribable grief for his family. Getting the mail became a dreaded ordeal. Day after day, they received the very letters they had sent to him while he was away. Each letter had been returned, unopened. All were stamped, *"Deceased-Return to Sender."*

For years after his death, my grandmother held onto the hope that the terrible news they received that afternoon was somehow a mistake. When a car door slammed shut, she would rush to the nearest window, hoping to see him walking up the driveway. She knew it would be a miracle if he returned home, yet we all knew she secretly prayed for that miracle until the day she passed away.

Fifteen years after Ronnie's death, a memorial was dedicated in Washington, D.C. to honor all the men and women who lost their lives in the Vietnam War. The names of the people who died or are missing in action are inscribed on the black stone wall. When my family visited the memorial that year, we searched for Ronnie's name among the other **58,000** names etched on the wall.

It was a beautiful sunny day. The sun reflected off the stone, which made it difficult for us to see. We looked and looked for Ronnie's name "I see it!" I yelled. My family wanted to make a pencil rubbing of his name so that we would have a keepsake to take home, but his name was too high on the wall for any of us to reach.

My brother climbed onto my dad's shoulders. He placed the paper over Ronnie's name and rubbed the pencil back and forth. When he climbed down, my brother handed the paper with his name on it to our grandfather. Pop stood quietly for a long time, staring at the paper without saying a word. That's when I noticed the tears in his eyes.

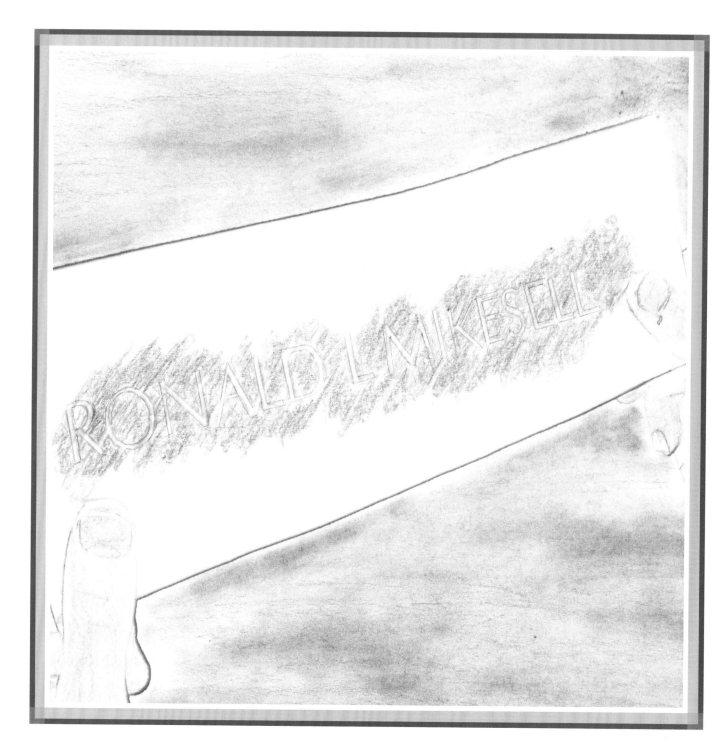

In America, we observe holidays like Memorial Day and Veteran's Day to honor all the individuals who have served our country, for their service and sacrifice.

It's been many years since I asked my mother about the man on the wall. I grew up, got married, and now I have children of my own. Recently, I took my sons to visit Ronnie's grave, so that they could learn of his courage and honor his memory.

As we placed flowers on his grave, my son asked, "Mom, who is it again that's buried here?" I paused for a moment, then crouched down next to him and explained, "That man was my uncle. He went to war and never came home. His name was Ronnie."

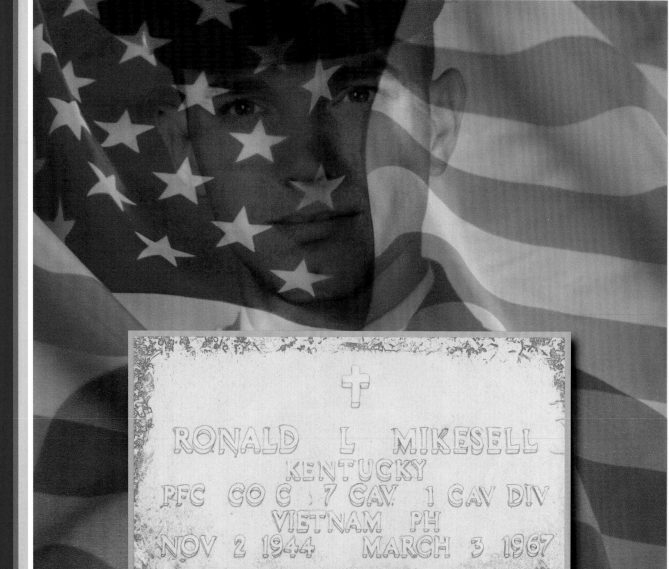

RONALD L. MIKESELL
KENTUCKY
PFC CO C 7 CAV 1 CAV DIV
VIETNAM PH
NOV 2 1944   MARCH 3 1967

Hi Honey

I don't have much time to write but I'll do what I can. They rushed us threw our training so fast I didn't have time to write. The training is usually 4 days, we got it in one. They must need us pretty bad. I'm at the Forward security now, at English Landing Zone. My company is in the field right now and I'll be going out by chopper in a couple of hours.

My address is right on the last letter you got so write as soon as you can. I don't think I can write too often but I'll keep in touch when I can. Call mama ever once in a while for me. I'll have a hard enough time writing you but I'll write them too when I can.

Well how are you doing? Have you started making my quilt yet? You better have me one when I get back. I haven't had a chance to go anywhere yet but when I do I'll send you something for our aniversary. By the way. When you send me that candy you promised me don't let it go over 10 pounds. If you do it will come over by boat and thats too slow. If you need any money or anything let me know and I'll send you some. I don't have anywhere to spend it so let me know if you need it.

...didn't get it.

Better go for now. I'll write when I can. Love and miss you very much. be good

Love ya
Ronnie
X X X X X

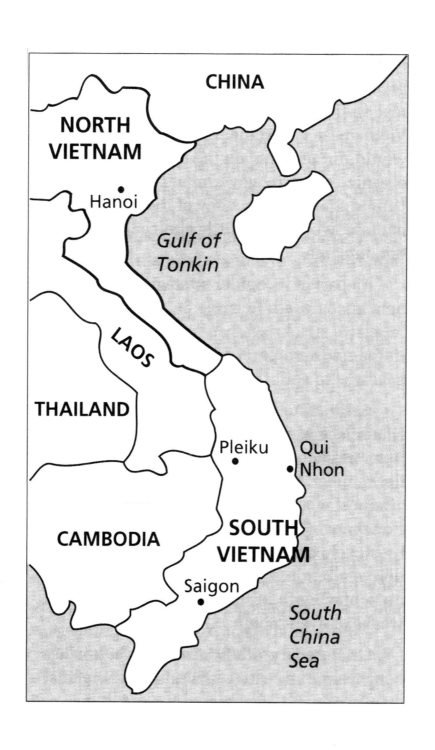

Timeline of Events Related to U.S. Involvement in the Vietnam War

1961 President Kennedy provides military experts and advisors to train the South Vietnamese troops.

1963 Vietnamese President Ngo Dihn Diem is assassinated.

1964 North Vietnam attacks an American military ship. The U.S. Congress grants President Lyndon B. Johnson the authority to use military force to protect itself from Vietnamese aggression.

1965 The United States begins air attacks in Vietnam and sends the first ground troops for combat.

1966 Nearly 400,000 Americans are engaged in the war in Vietnam.

1968 Formal peace talks take place but the war continues, with the growing number of Americans serving in the war estimated at 540,000.

1969 First American troop withdrawals.

1970 Troop withdrawals continue, but 280,000 Americans remain in Vietnam.

1973 A peace treaty is reached; a cease fire begins. The last American troops leave Vietnam.

1974 The war between North and South Vietnam resumes without the involvement of the United States.

1982 The Vietnam Memorial in Washington, D.C. is dedicated on November 11. More than 58,000 names of the service men and women who lost their lives are etched in the wall.

SOURCES:
Karnow, S. (1997). *Vietnam: A History*. Penguin Books, New York.
O'Nan, S. (Ed.), (1998). *The Vietnam Reader*. Anchor Books, New York.

Author's Note

This is my family's true story of love and loss. Although I have no personal memories of Ronnie, I chose to tell this story from my own perspective of what I've learned about him through the years. He left for Vietnam when I was only three months old. His death devastated his wife, parents, grandparents, eleven siblings and his extended family members and friends. In addition, he left behind 38 nieces and nephews who would never have the opportunity to know him. It is most important to remember that this is only one story. There are more than 58,000 other stories just like ours.

My uncle was not an aggressive individual, nor did he want to fight in Vietnam. At the same time, he never considered ignoring his call to serve. Like many men of his generation, he hoped he would not receive that letter from the Selective Service. When the letter arrived, he willingly accepted it as his responsibility. I don't know for certain, but I can only imagine that he was apprehensive at the thought of going off to war. Nonetheless, he projected a positive outlook around his family and friends, assuring everyone that he would complete his two years of service and return home, as both his father and older brother had done.

The anguish experienced by our soldiers in Vietnam has been well documented. Our family found some comfort in knowing that his time in Vietnam was short, and he was not subjected to months, or even years, of terrible and distressing conditions before his untimely death.

– CMG